Fractal Cosmic Curve: Tensor-Based Cosmos Theory

Stephen Blaha Ph. D.
Blaha Research

Pingree-Hill Publishing
MMXXIV

ISBN: 979-8-9858266-4-7

Rev. 00/00/01   February 18, 2024

To Margaret

Some Other Books by Stephen Blaha

SuperCivilizations: Civilizations as Superorganisms (McMann-Fisher Publishing, Auburn, NH, 2010)

All the Universe! Faster Than Light Tachyon Quark Starships & Particle Accelerators with the LHC as a Prototype Starship Drive Scientific Edition (Pingree-Hill Publishing, Auburn, NH, 2011).

Unification of God Theory and Unified SuperStandard Model THIRD EDITION (Pingree Hill Publishing, Auburn, NH, 2018).

The Exact QED Calculation of the Fine Structure Constant Implies ALL 4D Universes have the Same Physics/Life Prospects (Pingree Hill Publishing, Auburn, NH, 2019).

Passing Through Nature to Eternity ProtoCosmos, HyperCosmos, Unified SuperStandard Theory (Pingree Hill Publishing, Auburn, NH, 2022).

HyperCosmos Fractionation and Fundamental Reference Frame Based Unification: Particle Inner Space Basis of Parton and Dual Resonance Models (Pingree Hill Publishing, Auburn, NH, 2022).

The Cosmic Panorama: ProtoCosmos, HyperCosmos, Unified SuperStandard Theory (UST) Derivation (Pingree Hill Publishing, Auburn, NH, 2022).
Ultimate Origin: ProtoCosmos and HyperCosmos (Pingree Hill Publishing, Auburn, NH, 2022).

A New Completely Geometric SU(8) Cosmos Theory; New PseudoFermion Fields; Fibonacci-like Dimension Arrays; Ramsey Number Approximation (Pingree Hill Publishing, Auburn, NH, 2023).

God and and Cosmos Theory (Pingree Hill Publishing, Auburn, NH, 2023).

Newton's Apple is Now The Fermion (Pingree Hill Publishing, Auburn, NH, 2023).

Cosmos Theory: The Sub-Particle Gambol Model (Pingree Hill Publishing, Auburn, NH, 2023).

Cosmos-Universe-Particle-Gambol Theory (Pingree Hill Publishing, Auburn, NH, 2024).

Fractal Cosmos Theory (Pingree Hill Publishing, Auburn, NH, 2024).

Available on Amazon.com, bn.com Amazon.co.uk and other international web sites as well as at better bookstores.

CONTENTS

FIGURES and TABLES

Introduction

This book shows Cosmos Theory is directly based on a mathematical fact: the number of independent anti-symmetric tensors of 0, 1, 2, r indices in r even space-time dimensions. It removes the impression of some that Cosmos Theory is merely an aggregate of features without a sufficient cause.

It proceeds to show that Cosmos Theory emerges with a structure similar to Hilbert curve construction. The resulting Cosmic Curve has analogous features: the nesting of dimension arrays within dimension arrays and so on. The size of dimension arrays is set by the number of independent anti-symmetric tensors, which is a multiple of the number of creation and annihilation operators in a fermion in the various spaces. The result is a similar structuring of the Cosmos Curve, of dimension arrays, and of the gamma-matrices in our universe and in higher spaces. They all display similar nested features.

The book presents a concise description of new and known Cosmos Theory features. The fractal Cosmic Curve supports a unique Language that the book describes.

It also introduces a new SuperCosmos Theory that is a fractal curve construction whose elements are Cosmos Theories.

A major leap in the understanding of Cosmos features and their origin!

1. Tensor Origin of Cosmos Theory

Cosmos Theory, with all its implications, is based on one mathematical fact and two assumptions. The mathematical fact follows from a consideration of the representations of the homogeneous Lorenz group in four space-time dimensions extended to other space-time dimensions r.

There is a difference between undeniable mathematical fact and *ad hoc* hypotheses. The fact in question is the number of independent anti-symmetric tensors of 0, 1, 2, … , r indices in r even space-time dimensions;

$$2^r \tag{1.1}$$

This number equals the number of elements in an irreducible γ-matrix.[1] The number of rows (columns) of γ-matrices is

$$2^{r/2} \tag{1.2}$$

This number is also twice the number of spins in r dimensions for the fermion of lowest spin in r dimensions.[2]

If we consider the form of a fermion's quantum fields,[3] the first assumption:

$$\psi_1(x) = \Sigma_{\alpha,s}[b_1(\alpha, s)u_{\alpha s}f_\alpha(x) + d^\dagger_1(\alpha, s)v_{\alpha s}f_\alpha^*(x)] \tag{1.3}$$
$$\psi_2(x) = \Sigma_{\alpha,s}[b_2(\alpha, s)u_{\alpha s}f_\alpha(x) + d^\dagger_2(\alpha, s)v_{\alpha s}f_\alpha^*(x)]$$

where α represents the Fourier momentum, then the total number of creation and annihilation operators is

$$d_{cr} = 2^{r/2 + 2} \tag{1.4}$$

where an additional factor of 2 follows from taking account of the d and $d^\dagger$ operators and a second additional factor of 2 follows due to having two quantum fields.

The column length d_{cr} specifies degrees of freedom since the associated creation and annihilation operators generate independent states.

---

[1] For our universe where r = 4 the γ-matrices are the Dirac γ-matrices.
[2] The least spin fermion quantum field in a space-time of dimension r has the spin $s = \frac{1}{2}(2^{r/2 - 1} - 1)$.
[3] In our PseudoQuantum formulation of fermions in the 1970's and recvently we define two wave functions for each fermion for important reasoms presented in my earlier papers and books.

1.1 Dimension Arrays

We may define an array, the dimension array, by introducing a group index for a group with the same number of components as d_{cr} and use it to define a dimension array with d_{dr} elements:

$$d_{dr} = d_{cr}^2 = 2^{r+4} \tag{1.6}$$

The quantum fields with index a become:

$$\psi_{1a}(x) = \Sigma_{\alpha,s}[b_{1a}(\alpha, s)u_{\alpha s}f_\alpha(x) + d^\dagger_{1a}(\alpha, s)v_{\alpha s}f_\alpha^*(x)]$$
$$\psi_{2a}(x) = \Sigma_{\alpha,s}[b_{2a}(\alpha, s)u_{\alpha s}f_\alpha(x) + d^\dagger_{2a}(\alpha, s)v_{\alpha s}f_\alpha^*(x)]$$

The number of additional components is set equal to the number of operators, eq. 1.4, to give the group the same number of degrees of freedom. As a result d_{dr} may be represented in the form of a square array. We call it the *dimension array*. We define a space for each space-time dimension r with a corresponding dimension array. *We relate space dimensions to the set of creation/annihilation operators (with internal symmetries) since they both specify degrees of freedom.*

We make the second assumption:

We define spaces, which each have an associated dimension array that specifies a set of dimensions, and that specify the spectrum of each set of fundamental fermions, of scalar particles, and of symmetries (including space-time dimensions r and internal symmetry dimensions.)

Each space-time has an even number of dimensions. Odd space-time dimension cases are ruled out because they would have space-time dimension arrays that are redundant with the even space-time dimensions' dimension arrays. The numbers of their spins in odd dimensions are the same as the next lower even dimensions leading to redundant dimension arrays.

The dimension arrays and their associated spaces result.[4] We have called the theory of these spaces Cosmos Theory. Cosmos Theory is described in detail in our previous books.

The set of positive space-time dimension spaces ranges from r = 0 to r = ∞. We arbitrarily set the number of spaces with universes to ten. We may base this choice on a Planckian model for universes presented in Blaha (2024b).

Below we show that the column lengths of dimension arrays form a sequence that mirrors the piecewise linear elements of the fractal Hilbert curve leading us to characterize the HyperCosmos spaces as forming part of the *fractal Cosmiic Curve.*

---

[4] The appearance of powers of 2 is ultimately the result of the number of independent tensors in each space-time.

1.2 Extension of Spaces to Fractional Space-time Dimensions

The space-time dimensions that we have considered above are non-negative, even integer-valued dimensions greater than or equal to zero. We may introduce more dimensions by descending to negative dimensions as shown in Fig. 1.1. Spaces with negative integer dimensions are called the Limos spaces. They are used in gambol theory in Blaha (2024a).

We introduce positive (and now negative) Cayley-Dickson numbers n related to the positive (and negative) space-time dimensions r by

$$r = 2n - 2 \tag{1.7}$$

with the result

$$d_{cn} \equiv d_{cr} = 2^{n+1} = 2^{r/2+2} \tag{1.8}$$
$$d_{dn} \equiv d_{cr} = 2^{2n+2} = 2^{r+4} \tag{1.9}$$

We will use n to relate the dimension arrays to a Hilbert-like fractal curve.

Our ProtoCosmos model created a set of spaces (Fig. 1.1) with negative dimensions and fractional dimension arrays. We used them in our gambol studies (Blaha (2024a)) and to extend the Cosmos Curve to a zero dimension point. See below and Blaha (2024b).

1.3 The Fractal Cosmos Curve

We now use the fractal relations first found in Blaha (2024b). The fractal construction of the Cosmos Curve is based on the association of dimension array column lengths[5] and the orders of piecewise linear line segment lengths that are used to form a fractal curve. Eq. 1.10 relates the *Cosmos Curve* construction to the Hilbert curve construction.[6]

Cosmos Cayley-Dickson number $n = n_H - 1$ (1.10)
Hilbert Curve Line Length $= 2^{n_H}$
Hilbert Number of "boxes" $= 2^{2n_H}$
Cosmos Dimension Array Column Length $= 2^{n+1} = 2^{n_H}$
Cosmos Dimension Array Size (number of elements in array) $= 2^{2n+2} = 2^{2n_H}$

where n is the Cosmos Cayley-Dickson number and n_H is the order in the Hilbert curve construction. Figs. 1.2 – 1.4 show the map between Cosmos Curve diagrams and equivalent Hilbert curve diagrams.

The non-negative n (or r) dimension array column lengths combine to generate a two dimension filled square fractal grid from a one dimension line segment.

---

[5] Order by order (dimension by dimension) the dimension array column lengths map to the length of the corresponding Hilbert curve piecewise line lengths. Blaha (2024b).
[6] The construction of the fractal curve corresponding to Cosmos Theory spaces was shown to be similar to the construction of the Hilbert feactal curve in Blaha (2024b).

The negative n (r) dimension array column lengths for n = -2 through n = -∞ combine to form a one dimension line element of length 1 equal to the array column length 1 for n = -1 from a zero dimension point due to the identity

$$\sum_{n=1}^{\infty} 2^{-n} = 1 \qquad (1.11)$$

If we fully adjoin the dimension array column lengths for n = −∞ through n = ∞ then we have the *Cosmic Curve from a zero dimension point to a two dimension filled square grid.*

The fractal dimension generation is paralleled by the generation of dimension arrays at each step in its construction.

1.4 The Nesting of Cosmos Dimension Arrays

Figs. 1.2, 1.3, 1.7, 1.8, and 1.9 show the nesting of dimension arrays and Hilbert construction diagrams. For each n (and Hilbert order) the nth array (and diagram) contains four copies of the $(n-1)^{th}$ array (and diagram).

The nesting property carries through for the fermion spectrum and group symmetry arrays. Figs .1.4 and 1.5 show the nested fermion structure for our n = 3 universe. Figs .1.6 and 1.7 show the nested symmetry group structure for our n = 3 universe. Figs. 1.8 and 1.9 show the nested dimension array structure for the n = 4 Megaverse.

The nesting of the group symmetries is modified after the quartering (or quadrupling) to connect various quarters together. Some of the symmetry groups are defined to connect quarters together using Connection Groups that we have described in earlier books such as Blaha (2023d).

If one considers the known Standard Model part within these diagrams one sees it fits in the nested dimension arrays like the pieces in a puzzle. Thus there is experimental support for Cosmos Theory in The Standard Model.

1.5 Euclidean View of the Creation of Cosmos Theory

With the basis of Cosmos Theory in the tensor structure of spaces we now have a complete theory with fundamental assumptions and a construction process modeled on the fractal Cosmic Curve that parallels Euclid's formulation of Geometry. The theory is purely mathematical: a mirror of Reality.

1.6 Analogous γ-Matrix Features

The even space-time dimension γ-matrices exhibit properties similar to the Cosmos Theory dimension arrays:

1. Dimension arrays have a size that is 16 times the size of γ-matrices.

2. The γ-matrices are square. They are r matrices of size $2^{r/2}$ by $2^{r/2}$. As the even space-time dimension r increases by 2 the γ-matrices row and column sizes

double. The γ-matrices quadruple as a result. For example the r = 6 γ-matrices are 8 by 8 matrices containing a quadruple of r = 4 γ-matrix parts.

3. The γ-matrices exhibit a form of nesting in quadruples. Fig. 1.10 displays nesting from r =2 (Pauli matrices) to r = 4 and then to r =6 quadrupling at each dimension increase by 2.

4. Fractional γ-matrices of negative dimension n may be defined by quartering the γ-matrices of the next higher space-time dimension. These fractional matrices may be of interest for gambol quantum field theory. This topic has been considered in our previous books.

The Hilbert curve features, Cosmos dimension array features, and γ-matrix structural features are the same.

1.7 Second Kind HyperCosmos Spaces

The Second Kind HyperCosmos spaces are generated with dimension arrays that are half the size of HyperCosmos dimension arrays. They may be interpreted as the same as HyperCosmos dimension arrays but without a Dark sector. Their n^{th} space dimension array size d_{dN2} is (Fig. 1.1)

$$d_{d2n} = 2^{r+3} \qquad (1.12)$$

See Blaha (2024a) and earlier books for details.

1.8 The Cosmic Curve and Unification and Fundamental Reference Frame (FRF)

In Blaha (2023a) we developed a unification of the ten HyperCosmos spaces and the 10 Second Kind HyperCosmos in a 42 space-time dimension Full HyperUnification space. See Fig. 1.11. The purpose was to create a space from these 20 spaces that supported a combined General Relativistic and symmetry group transformation that would generate the dimension arrays of all 20 spaces from one dimension located in a Fundamental Reference Frame (FRF).

In section 3.3.1 0f Blaha (2023a) we described the nature of an FRF. A dimension array Reference Frame treats a dimension array with d_{dr} components as a vector. The vector is subject to a combined General Relativistic – Internal Symmetry transformation to produce a new dimension array in vector form. One may chose the Reference Frame to be an FRF where the vector has only one non-zero dimension. This FRF is analogous to the rest frame of a particle with only one non-zero momentum component: its energy equals its mass. The analogy to Special Relativistic transformations from a rest frame to a moving frame is clear.

Using FRF's allows the dimension array of any space to be reduced to one non-zero component.

An examination of Fig. 1.11 shows that the 10 dimension arrays' column lengths and 10 Second Kind HyperCosmos dimension arrays' column lengths combine to form the 42 space-time dimension Full HyperUnification space shown in Fig. 1.12. The column lengths of the HyperCosmos part are a subset of the column lengths in the Cosmic Curve. See Blaha (2023a) for details.

The dimension array of the 42 space-time dimension Full HyperUnification space can be treated as a vector in an 88 space-time dimension UltraUnification (UU) space. Then an FRF may be defined for it with only one non-zero dimension that enables the UU dimension array to be generated from the FRF with only one non-zero dimension.

Thus the UU gives a reduction of all Cosmos Theory dimension arrays to one primordial non-zero dimension – an ultimate form of unification of all Cosmos Theory spaces. See Fig. 1.12 for the structure of the complete set of Cosmos spaces. There are four levels in the Cosmos, which is the most economical approach to generating the Cosmos. The one primordial dimension in UU can be fractionated into an infinite dust of fractionated dimensions using Limos.

The spaces of Cosmos Theory (Fig. 1.12) *are*

$$\begin{aligned}
&!0 \text{ HyperCosmos spaces + their 10 HyperUnification spaces +} \qquad (1.13)\\
&+ !0 \text{ Second Kind HyperCosmos spaces +}\\
&+ \text{ the 10 Second Kind HyperUnification spaces +}\\
&+ \text{ the 42 Dimension Full HyperUnification Space +}\\
&+ \text{ the 88 Dimension UU space = 42 spaces}\\
&+ \text{ Limos}^7 (\text{not shown in Fig. 1.12})
\end{aligned}$$

1.9 The Two Dimension Square Grid

The Cosmic Curve generates a two dimension filled square grid. This grid might be viewed as the beginning of a new Cosmos spaces spectrum. It embodies the 4 dimensions of the 2×2 n = 0 dimension array d_{d0}, which is the precursor of the ten HyperCosmos spaces. It might be viewed as a continuous grid corresponding to d_{d0}.

The four corners of the Cosmic Curve square grid is mapped to the four dimensions of an n = 0 dimension array. We can associate that dimension array with the $n_H = 1$ Hilbert order diagram and proceed to construct a new Hilbert-like curve and a new associated sets of Cosmos dimension arrays from it. At each order of construction we take the boxes of type C in Fig. 1.2 and transform them to boxes of type D filling each with a "color pattern." As the order n_H increases, an irregularly shaped figure is generated that becomes a set of interconnected islands of "Cosmic" color.

This new construction of interconnected islands might be called a *SuperCosmos* archipelago. It corresponds order by order to supersets of Cosmos spaces with filled grids used to introduce continuity between dimensions in each 4 by 4 block. Thus a continuum is established between the elements of each diagram. The elements are, of course, Cosmos Theory sets of spaces.

---

[77] Limos spaces with their negative space-time dimensions are not part of the Full HyperUnification space or the UltraUnification space because they do not participate in the unification of the twenty HyperCosmos spaces.

1.10 The Language of the Cosmic Curve

The Hilbert curve and thus the Cosmic Curve may be viewed as generated according to a language ((L System). The language specification is

Alphabet: α, β
Constants: φ + −
 Axiom: α

Production Rules:
α → +βφ–αφα − φβ+
β→ −αφ+βφβ+φα-

The language interpretation of the Hilbert and Coamic Curves introduces an interesting new view of Cosmos Theory raising the issue of a Cosmic Language. Languages have been associated with Physics previously. See Blaha (1998) and (2005c) for detailed examples.

1.11 Comparison between Fractal Formulation and Creation/Annihilation Operator Formulation

The fractal formulation, and the creation/annihilation operator based formulation, offer somewhat different approaches to Cosmos Theory. The fractal formulation, which has a Hilbert-like curve view: the Cosmic Curve, offers the perhaps a simpler, more elegant formulation. The fractal formulation has the same nesting as the Cosmos Theory dimension arrays.

The fractal formulation does not have some significant features of the Creation/Annihilation Operator (CAO) formulation :

1. ***The basis of the CAO formulation in the number of independent tensors singles out the CAO formulation as fundamental.***

2. The choice of even number space-time dimensions only is natural in the CAO formulation since the total number of creation and annihilation operators in an odd dimension space equals the number in the next lower even dimension – thus giving a potential redundancy that is removed by choosing even dimensions only.

3. The CAO formulation creates a dimension array that has extended General Relativistic – Internal Symmetry transformations that parallel the corresponding transformations of the creation/annihilation operators of fermion fields.in General Relativity.

4.   The CAO formulation allows one to define a Fundamental Reference Frame (FRF) that can map a single primordial dimension to complete dimension arrays, which introduces a fundamental simplicity in the Cosmos.

5.   Space-time dimensions may be extracted from a dimension array using eq. 1.2.

6.   Manipulation of the quantum fields based on the CAO formalism enables the creation of totally unified quantum field theories through the generation of 42 and 88 space-time dimension spaces.

We conclude the CAO tensor-based formalism is the correct basis for Cosmos Theory and the UST for our universe.

1.12 Future Directions

The fundamental fact of Cosmos Theory, the number of independent tensors in a space, and the assumptions that then lead directly to the Cosmos spaces spectrum, make Cosmos Theory the most likely theory of the Cosmos.

This conclusion motivates the following program for Elementary Particles:

1.   Study other additional features of Cosmos Theory.

2.   Perform experiments to expand the fermion spectrum to a fourth generation and to three additional layers.

3.   Explore the implications of the Generation and Layer groups – particularly for the expansion of the Cabibbo-Kobayashi-Maskawa (CKM) matrix

4.   Look for Astrophysical support for Cosmos Theory – particularly for the Megaverse and higher dimension universes.

The spectrum of particles and symmetries needs to be expanded from The Standard Model to the predictions of Cosmos Theory and the Unified SuperStandard Theory (UST).

Success in these endeavors will lead to a new Physics. The possibility of several new accelerators operating at 3 to 8 times current maximum energies is encouraging.

This author *solely* developed Cosmos Theory over the past five years beginning with The Standard Model, and with his previous work.

He followed the path:

The Standard Model $\rightarrow$

   Unified SuperStandard Theory $\rightarrow$

      Hypercomplex number based extensions $\rightarrow$

         Cosmos Theory $\rightarrow$

            Fractal Cosmos Curve Theory $\rightarrow$

               Tensor based Fractal Cosmos Theory

COSMOS SPACES SPECTRUM

Blaha Space Number $N = o_s$	Cayley-Dickson Number n	Cayley Number d_c	Dimension Array column length d_{cn}	Dimension Array Size d_{dn}	Space-time-Dimension r
0	10	1024	2048	2048^2	18
1	9	512	1024	1024^2	16
2	8	256	512	512^2	14
3	7	128	256	256^2	12
4	6	64	128	128^2	10
5	5	32	64	64^2	8
6	4	16	32	32^2	6
7	**3**	**8**	**16**	**16^2**	**4**
8	2	4	8	8^2	2
9	1	2	4	4^2	0
10	0	1	2	2^2	-2
Limos :					
11	-1	½	1	1	-4
12	-2	¼	½	$½^2$	-6
13	-3	1/8	¼	$¼^2$	-8
14	-4	1/16	1/8	$1/8^2$	-10

•
•
•

HYPERCOSMOS OF THE SECOND KIND SPACES SPECTRUM

Blaha Space Number $N = O_s$	Cayley-Dickson Number n	Cayley Number d_c	Dimension Array size d_{dN2}	Space-time-Dimension r	CASe Group $su(2^{r/2}, 2^{r/2})$ CASe
0	10	1024	1024×2048	18	su(512,512)
1	9	512	512×1024	16	su(256,256)
2	8	256	256×512	14	su(128,128)
3	7	128	128×256	12	su(64,64)
4	6	64	64×128	10	su(32,32)
5	5	32	32×64	8	su(16,16)
6	4	16	16×32	6	su(8,8)
7	**3**	**8**	**8×16**	**4**	**su(4,4)**
8	2	4	4×8	2	su(2,2)
9	1	2	2×4	0	su(1,1)
10	0	1	1×2	-2	
11	-2	½	½	-4	

Figure 1.1. The HyperCosmos, Limos, and the HyperCosmos of the Second Kind, space spectrums.

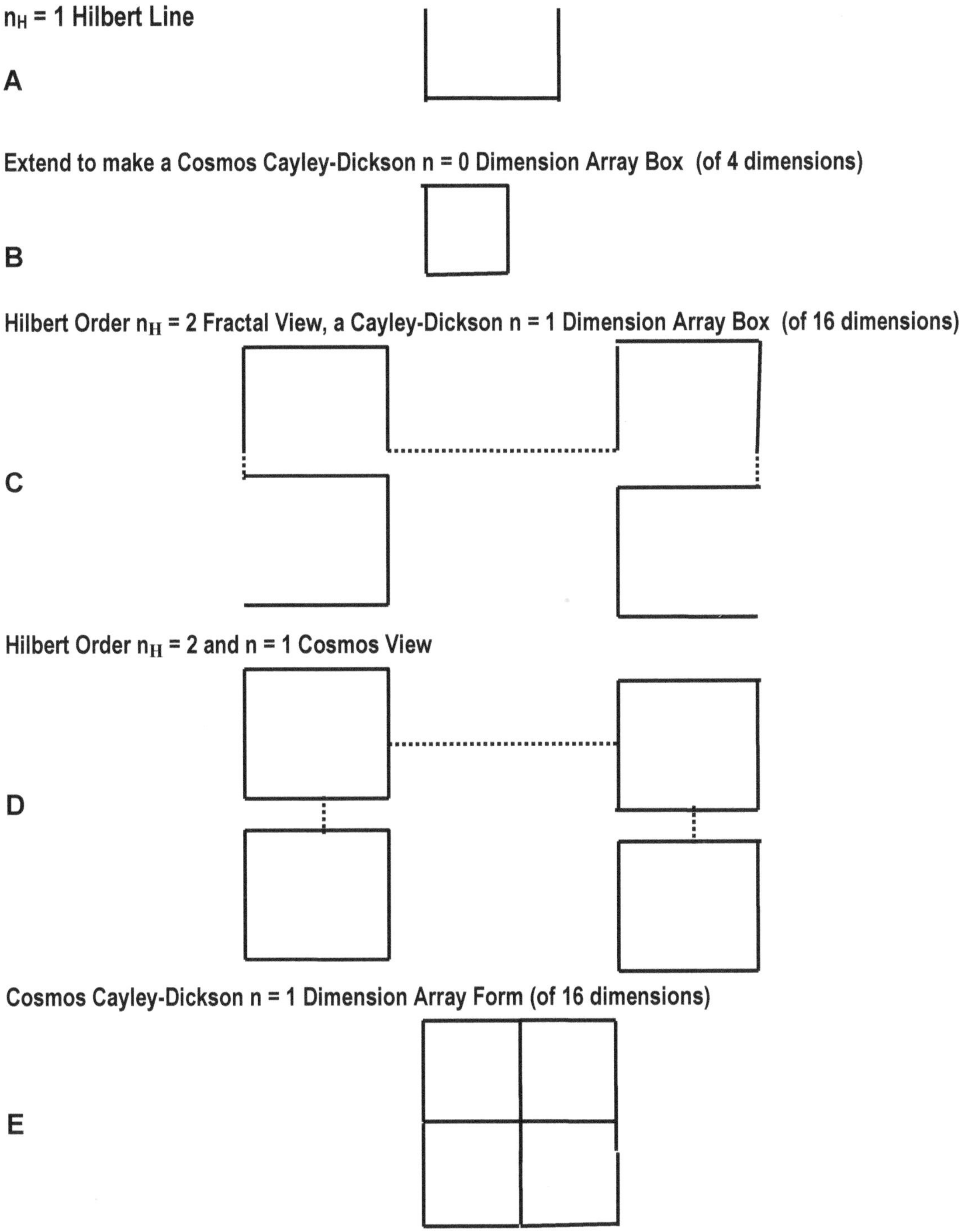

$n_H = 1$ Hilbert Line

A

Extend to make a Cosmos Cayley-Dickson n = 0 Dimension Array Box (of 4 dimensions)

B

Hilbert Order $n_H = 2$ Fractal View, a Cayley-Dickson n = 1 Dimension Array Box (of 16 dimensions)

C

Hilbert Order $n_H = 2$ and n = 1 Cosmos View

D

Cosmos Cayley-Dickson n = 1 Dimension Array Form (of 16 dimensions)

E

Figure 1.2. The transition from the Hilbert curve Fractal diagrams to the Cosmos Theory dimension array diagrams. Every Hilbert fractal diagram has an equivalent Cosmos Theory dimension array.

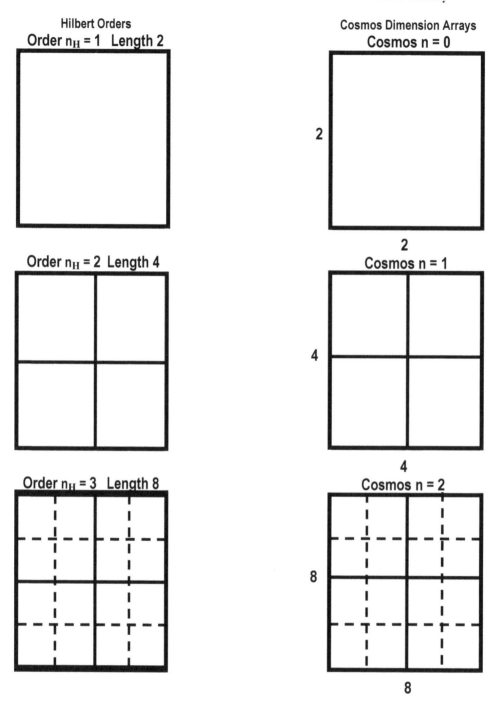

Figure 1.3. Low order Hilbert line segments depicted as nested sets of boxes as in Fig. 1.2 compared to corresponding Cosmos Theory dimension arrays ordered by Cayley-Dickson numbers. Dimension array sizes are displayed.

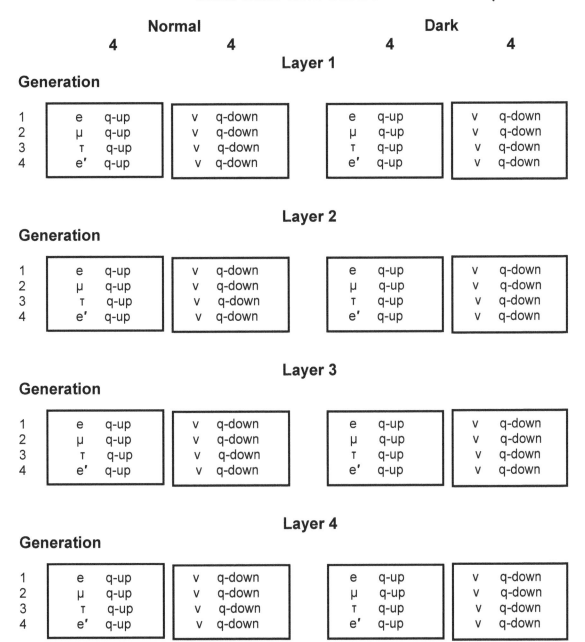

Figure 1.4. Periodic table for the Normal and Dark fermions of UST. Each fermion corresponds to a dimension. Subscripts of neutrinos and quarks are not shown. A fourth generation is indicated for each layer. There are 256 fermions corresponding to the 256 entries in the dimension array for n = 3. This figure is from Blaha (2020d) for the UST. The nesting in 4×4 blocks is evident within 8×8 blocks within a 16×16 block.

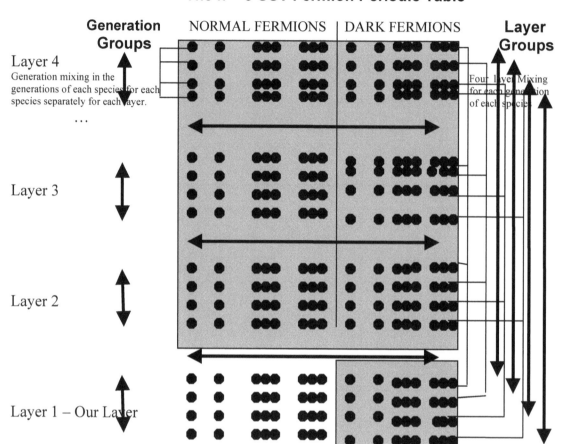

Figure 1.5. Fermion particle spectrum and partial example of pattern of mass mixing of the Generation and Layer grroups. Unshaded parts are the known fermions including an additional, as yet not found, 4th generation shown. The lines on the left side (only shown for one layer) display the Generation mixing within each layer's species. The Generation mixing applies within each layer using a separate Generation group for each layer. The lines on the right side show Layer group mixing with the mixing amongst all four layers for each of the four generations individually. There are four Layer groups. For each generation and each layer, SU(2)⊗U(1) mixes between an e-type fermion and a neutrino-type fermion. It also mixes between an up-quark-type fermion and a down-quark-type fermion. SU(3) mixes among each up-quark triplet and down-quark triplet separately. Complex Lorentz group transformations map among all four fermions: Dirac ↔ tachyon ↔ up-quark ↔ down-quark There are 256 fundamental fermions counting quarks as triplets. This figure is from Blaha (2020e) for the UST.

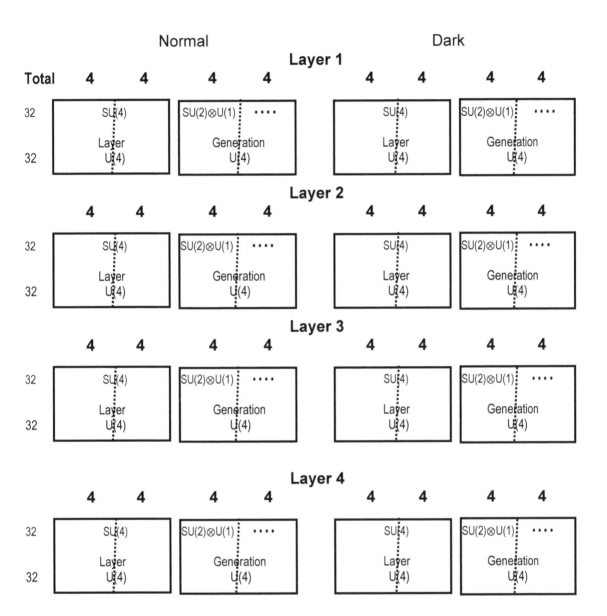

Figure 1.6. Schematic for the Normal and Dark symmetries of UST. The real and imaginary dimensions are counted separately. For example SU(4) has four real dimensions and four imaginary dimensions. Each layer has 32 + 32 = 64 dimensions. There are 256 dimensions corresponding to the 256 entries in the dimension array for UST where n = 3. The 32 • 's form sets of 4 dimensions were allocated initially to 4D space-times. These dots are mapped to SL(2, **C**) and 7 SU(2)⊗U(1) Connection groups in Fig. 1.7. Three groups unite layers, and 4 groups unite corresponding Normal and Dark layers This figure is from Blaha (2020d) for the UST.

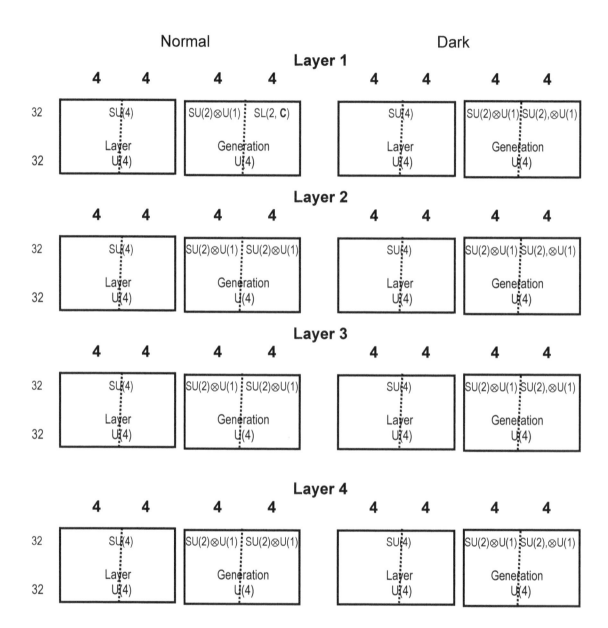

Figure 1.7. Schematic for the Normal and Dark symmetries of UST. Seven sets of dots in Fig. 1.6 are replaced by SU(2)⊗U(1) Connection groups. SL(2, C) represents the Lorentz group SO⁺(1,3). This figure is from Blaha (2020d) for the UST.

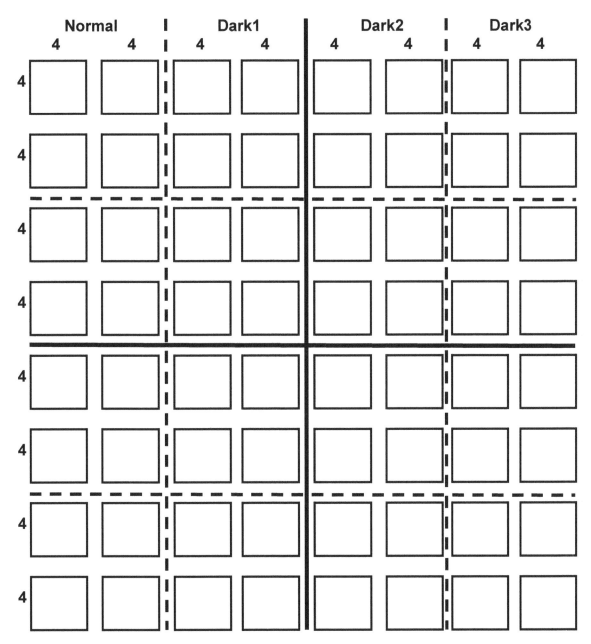

Figure 1.8. The n = 4 Megaverse dimension array. Four quadruplings are visible. Each quadrant is an n = 3 UST dimension array. There are sixty-four 4 × 4 n = 1 blocks. Each 8 × 8 quadrant is an n = 2 dimension array. Each 16 × 16 quadrant is an n = 3 dimension array. An exact match with Hilbert orders nesting is evident. This figure is from Blaha (2020d) for the UST.

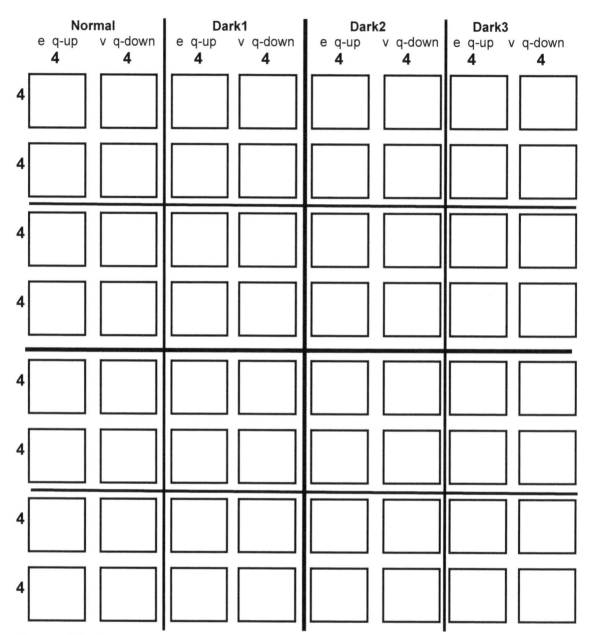

Figure 1.9. Partition of the fermion 32 × 32 Cayley-Dickson n = 4 (Megaverse) dimension array. Four quadruples are visible. There are sixty-four 4 × 4 n = 1 blocks. Each 8 × 8 quadrant is an n = 2 dimension array. Each 16 × 16 quadrant is an n = 3 dimension array. An exact match with Hilbert orders is evident. The label e q-up indicates a charged lepton – up-type quark pair. The label v q-down indicates a neutral lepton – down-type quark pair, and so on. This figure is from Blaha (2020i) for the UST and Megaverse.

r = 4

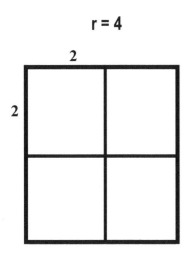

r = 6

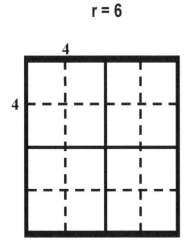

Figure 1.10. The γ-matrices for r = 4 and r = 6 space-time dimensions. The matrices exhibit a nested structure quadrupling as the dimension increases by 2. For example, the r = 4 γ-matrices contain the r = 2 Pauli matrices.

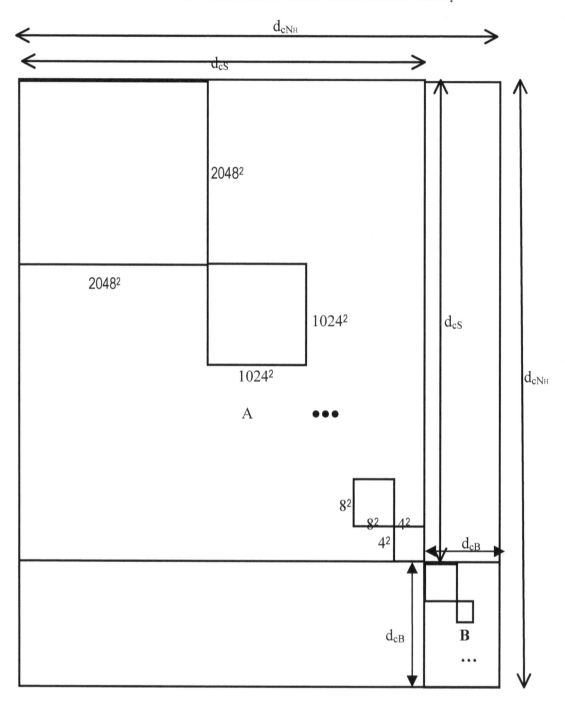

Figure 1.11. Form of a HyperUnification transformation. It is also the form of the dimension array of 42 dimension space-time. Ten HyperCosmos dimension array's column lengths are shown. Ten Second Kind HyperCosmos dimension array's column lengths are contained in the d_{cB} by d_{cB} block. The figure is not drawn to scale. See Chapter 6 of Blaha (2023a) for details.

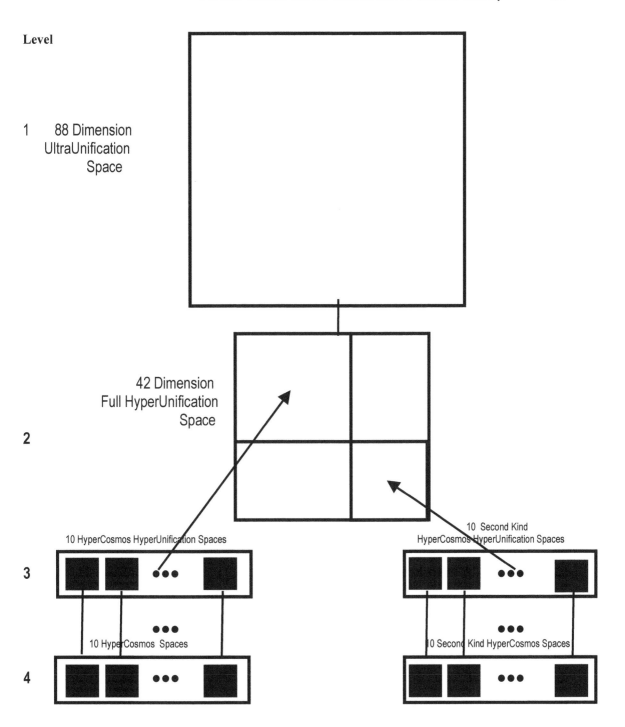

Figure 1.12. Diagram of the four levels of the Cosmos Spaces. They contain 42 spaces with no contributions from Limos spaces which are treated separately.

REFERENCES

Akhiezer, N. I., Frink, A. H. (tr), 1962, *The Calculus of Variations* (Blaisdell Publishing, New York, 1962).

Bjorken, J. D., Drell, S. D., 1964, *Relativistic Quantum Mechanics* (McGraw-Hill, New York, 1965).

Bjorken, J. D., Drell, S. D., 1965, *Relativistic Quantum Fields* (McGraw-Hill, New York, 1965).

Blaha, S., 1995, *C++ for Professional Programming* (International Thomson Publishing, Boston, 1995).

_____, 1998, *Cosmos and Consciousness* (Pingree-Hill Publishing, Auburn, NH, 1998 and 2002).

_____, 2002, *A Finite Unified Quantum Field Theory of the Elementary Particle Standard Model and Quantum Gravity Based on New Quantum Dimensions™ & a New Paradigm in the Calculus of Variations* (Pingree-Hill Publishing, Auburn, NH, 2002).

_____, 2004, *Quantum Big Bang Cosmology: Complex Space-time General Relativity, Quantum Coordinates™ Dodecahedral Universe, Inflation, and New Spin 0, ½, 1 & 2 Tachyons & Imagyons* (Pingree-Hill Publishing, Auburn, NH, 2004).

_____, 2005a, *Quantum Theory of the Third Kind: A New Type of Divergence-free Quantum Field Theory Supporting a Unified Standard Model of Elementary Particles and Quantum Gravity based on a New Method in the Calculus of Variations* (Pingree-Hill Publishing, Auburn, NH, 2005).

_____, 2005b, *The Metatheory of Physics Theories, and the Theory of Everything as a Quantum Computer Language* (Pingree-Hill Publishing, Auburn, NH, 2005).

_____, 2005c, *The Equivalence of Elementary Particle Theories and Computer Languages: Quantum Computers, Turing Machines, Standard Model, Superstring Theory, and a Proof that Gödel's Theorem Implies Nature Must Be Quantum* (Pingree-Hill Publishing, Auburn, NH, 2005).

_____, 2006a, *The Foundation of the Forces of Nature* (Pingree-Hill Publishing, Auburn, NH, 2006).

_____, 2006b, *A Derivation of ElectroWeak Theory based on an Extension of Special Relativity; Black Hole Tachyons; & Tachyons of Any Spin.* (Pingree-Hill Publishing, Auburn, NH, 2006).

_____, 2007a, *Physics Beyond the Light Barrier: The Source of Parity Violation, Tachyons, and A Derivation of Standard Model Features* (Pingree-Hill Publishing, Auburn, NH, 2007).

_____, 2007b, *The Origin of the Standard Model: The Genesis of Four Quark and Lepton Species, Parity Violation, the ElectroWeak Sector, Color SU(3), Three Visible Generations of Fermions, and One Generation of Dark Matter with Dark Energy* (Pingree-Hill Publishing, Auburn, NH, 2007).

_____, 2008a, *A Direct Derivation of the Form of the Standard Model From GL(16)* (Pingree-Hill Publishing, Auburn, NH, 2008).

_____, 2008b, *A Complete Derivation of the Form of the Standard Model With a New Method to Generate Particle Masses Second Edition* (Pingree-Hill Publishing, Auburn, NH, 2008)

_____, 2009, *The Algebra of Thought & Reality: The Mathematical Basis for Plato's Theory of Ideas, and Reality Extended to Include A Priori Observers and Space-Time Second Edition* (Pingree-Hill Publishing, Auburn, NH, 2009).

26 **REFERENCES**

_____, 2010a, *Operator Metaphysics: A New Metaphysics Based on a New Operator Logic and a New Quantum Operator Logic that Lead to a Mathematical Basis for Plato's Theory of Ideas and Reality* (Pingree-Hill Publishing, Auburn, NH, 2010).

_____, 2010b, *The Standard Model's Form Derived from Operator Logic, Superluminal Transformations and GL(16)* (Pingree-Hill Publishing, Auburn, NH, 2010).

_____, 2010c, *SuperCivilizations: Civilizations as Superorganisms* (McMann-Fisher Publishing, Auburn, NH, 2010).

_____, 2011a, *21*st *Century Natural Philosophy Of Ultimate Physical Reality* (McMann-Fisher Publishing, Auburn, NH, 2011).

_____, 2011b, *All the Universe! Faster Than Light Tachyon Quark Starships & Particle Accelerators with the LHC as a Prototype Starship Drive Scientific Edition* (Pingree-Hill Publishing, Auburn, NH, 2011).

_____, 2011c, *From Asynchronous Logic to The Standard Model to Superflight to the Stars* (Blaha Research, Auburn, NH, 2011).

_____, 2012a, *From Asynchronous Logic to The Standard Model to Superflight to the Stars volume 2: Superluminal CP and CPT, U(4) Complex General Relativity and The Standard Model, Complex Vierbein General Relativity, Kinetic Theory, Thermodynamics* (Blaha Research, Auburn, NH, 2012).

_____, 2012b, *Standard Model Symmetries, And Four And Sixteen Dimension Complex Relativity; The Origin Of Higgs Mass Terms* (Blaha Reasearch, Auburn, NH, 2012).

_____, 2013a, *Multi-Stage Space Guns, Micro-Pulse Nuclear Rockets, and Faster-Than-Light Quark-Gluon Ion Drive Starships* (Blaha Research, Auburn, NH, 2013).

_____, 2013b, *The Bridge to Dark Matter; A New Sibling Universe; Dark Energy; Inflatons; Quantum Big Bang; Superluminal Physics; An Extended Standard Model Based on Geometry* (Blaha Reasearch, Auburn, NH, 2013).

_____, 2014a, *Universes and Megaverses: From a New Standard Model to a Physical Megaverse; The Big Bang; Our Sibling Universe's Wormhole; Origin of the Cosmological Constant, Spatial Asymmetry of the Universe, and its Web of Galaxies; A Baryonic Field between Universes and Particles; Megaverse Extended Wheeler-DeWitt Equation* (Blaha Reasearch, Auburn, NH, 2014).

_____, 2014b, *All the Megaverse! Starships Exploring the Endless Universes of the Cosmos Using the Baryonic Force* (Blaha Research, Auburn, NH, 2014).

_____, 2014c, *All the Megaverse! II Between Megaverse Universes: Quantum Entanglement Explained by the Megaverse Coherent Baryonic Radiation Devices – PHASERs Neutron Star Megaverse Slingshot Dynamics Spiritual and UFO Events, and the Megaverse Microscopic Entry into the Megaverse* (Blaha Research, Auburn, NH, 2014).

_____, 2015a, *PHYSICS IS LOGIC PAINTED ON THE VOID: Origin of Bare Masses and The Standard Model in Logic, U(4) Origin of the Generations, Normal and Dark Baryonic Forces, Dark Matter, Dark Energy, The Big Bang, Complex General Relativity, A Megaverse of Universe Particles* (Blaha Research, Auburn, NH, 2015).

_____, 2015b, *PHYSICS IS LOGIC Part II: The Theory of Everything, The Megaverse Theory of Everything, U(4)⊗U(4) Grand Unified Theory (GUT), Inertial Mass = Gravitational Mass, Unified Extended Standard Model and a New Complex General Relativity with Higgs Particles, Generation Group Higgs Particles* (Blaha Research, Auburn, NH, 2015).

_____, 2015c, *The Origin of Higgs ("God") Particles and the Higgs Mechanism: Physics is Logic III, Beyond Higgs – A Revamped Theory With a Local Arrow of Time, The Theory of Everything Enhanced, Why Inertial Frames are Special, Universes of the Mind* (Blaha Research, Auburn, NH, 2015).

_____, 2015d, *The Origin of the Eight Coupling Constants of The Theory of Everything: U(8) Grand Unified Theory of Everything (GUTE), S^8 Coupling Constant Symmetry, Space-Time Dependent Coupling Constants, Big Bang Vacuum Coupling Constants, Physics is Logic IV* (Blaha Research, Auburn, NH, 2015).

_____, 2016a, *New Types of Dark Matter, Big Bang Equipartition, and A New U(4) Symmetry in the Theory of Everything: Equipartition Principle for Fermions, Matter is 83.33% Dark, Penetrating the Veil of the Big Bang, Explicit QFT Quark Confinement and Charmonium, Physics is Logic V* (Blaha Research, Auburn, NH, 2016).

_____, 2016b, *The Periodic Table of the 192 Quarks and Leptons in The Theory of Everything: The U(4) Layer Group, Physics is Logic VI* (Blaha Research, Auburn, NH, 2016).

_____, 2016c, *New Boson Quantum Field Theory, Dark Matter Dynamics, Dark Matter Fermion Layer Mixing, Genesis of Higgs Particles, New Layer Higgs Masses, Higgs Coupling Constants, Non-Abelian Higgs Gauge Fields, Physics is Logic VII* (Blaha Research, Auburn, NH, 2016).

_____, 2016d, *Unification of the Strong Interactions and Gravitation: Quark Confinement Linked to Modified Short-Distance Gravity; Physics is Logic VIII* (Blaha Research, Auburn, NH, 2016).

_____, 2016e, *MoND: Unification of the Strong Interactions and Gravitation II, Quark Confinement Linked to Large-Scale Gravity, Physics is Logic IX* (Blaha Research, Auburn, NH, 2016).

_____, 2016f, *CQ Mechanics: A Unification of Quantum & Classical Mechanics, Quantum/Semi-Classical Entanglement, Quantum/Classical Path Integrals, Quantum/Classical Chaos* (Blaha Research, Auburn, NH, 2016).

_____, 2016g, *GEMS Unified Gravity, ElectroMagnetic and Strong Interactions: Manifest Quark Confinement, A Solution for the Proton Spin Puzzle, Modified Gravity on the Galactic Scale* (Pingree Hill Publishing, Auburn, NH, 2016).

_____, 2016h, *Unification of the Seven Boson Interactions based on the Riemann-Christoffel Curvature Tensor* (Pingree Hill Publishing, Auburn, NH, 2016).

_____, 2017a, *Unification of the Eleven Boson Interactions based on 'Rotations of Interactions'* (Pingree Hill Publishing, Auburn, NH, 2017).

_____, 2017b, *The Origin of Fermions and Bosons, and Their Unification* (Pingree Hill Publishing, Auburn, NH, 2017).

_____, 2017c, *Megaverse: The Universe of Universes* (Pingree Hill Publishing, Auburn, NH, 2017).

_____, 2017d, *SuperSymmetry and the Unified SuperStandard Model* (Pingree Hill Publishing, Auburn, NH, 2017).

_____, 2017e, *From Qubits to the Unified SuperStandard Model with Embedded SuperStrings: A Derivation* (Pingree Hill Publishing, Auburn, NH, 2017).

_____, 2017f, *The Unified SuperStandard Model in Our Universe and the Megaverse: Quarks, ... ,* (Pingree Hill Publishing, Auburn, NH, 2017).

_____, 2018a, *The Unified SuperStandard Model and the Megaverse SECOND EDITION A Deeper Theory based on a New Particle Functional Space that Explicates Quantum Entanglement Spookiness (Volume 1)* (Pingree Hill Publishing, Auburn, NH, 2018).

_____, 2018b, *Cosmos Creation: The Unified SuperStandard Model, Volume 2, SECOND EDITION* (Pingree Hill Publishing, Auburn, NH, 2018).

_____, 2018c, *God Theory (*Pingree Hill Publishing, Auburn, NH, 2018).

_____, 2018d, *Immortal Eye: God Theory: Second Edition* (Pingree Hill Publishing, Auburn, NH, 2018).

_____, 2018e, *Unification of God Theory and Unified SuperStandard Model THIRD EDITION* (Pingree Hill Publishing, Auburn, NH, 2018).

_____, 2019a, *Calculation of: QED α = 1/137, and Other Coupling Constants of the Unified SuperStandard Theory* (Pingree Hill Publishing, Auburn, NH, 2019).

_____, 2019b, *Coupling Constants of the Unified SuperStandard Theory SECOND EDITION* (Pingree Hill Publishing, Auburn, NH, 2019).

_____, 2019c, *New Hybrid Quantum Big_Bang–Megaverse_Driven Universe with a Finite Big Bang and an Increasing Hubble Constant* (Pingree Hill Publishing, Auburn, NH, 2019).

_____, 2019d, *The Universe, The Electron and The Vacuum* (Pingree Hill Publishing, Auburn, NH, 2019).

_____, 2019e, *Quantum Big Bang – Quantum Vacuum Universes (Particles)* (Pingree Hill Publishing, Auburn, NH, 2019).

_____, 2019f, *The Exact QED Calculation of the Fine Structure Constant Implies ALL 4D Universes have the Same Physics/Life Prospects* (Pingree Hill Publishing, Auburn, NH, 2019).

_____, 2019g, *Unified SuperStandard Theory and the SuperUniverse Model: The Foundation of Science* (Pingree Hill Publishing, Auburn, NH, 2019).

_____, 2020a, *Quaternion Unified SuperStandard Theory (The QUeST) and Megaverse Octonion SuperStandard Theory (MOST)* (Pingree Hill Publishing, Auburn, NH, 2020).

_____, 2020b, *United Universes Quaternion Universe - Octonion Megaverse* (Pingree Hill Publishing, Auburn, NH, 2020).

_____, 2020c, *Unified SuperStandard Theories for Quaternion Universes & The Octonion Megaverse* (Pingree Hill Publishing, Auburn, NH, 2020).

_____, 2020d, *The Essence of Eternity: Quaternion & Octonion SuperStandard Theories* (Pingree Hill Publishing, Auburn, NH, 2020).

_____, 2020e, *The Essence of Eternity II* (Pingree Hill Publishing, Auburn, NH, 2020).

_____, 2020f, *A Very Conscious Universe* (Pingree Hill Publishing, Auburn, NH, 2020).

_____, 2020g, *Hypercomplex Universe* (Pingree Hill Publishing, Auburn, NH, 2020).

_____, 2020h, *Beneath the Quaternion Universe* (Pingree Hill Publishing, Auburn, NH, 2020).

_____, 2020i, *Why is the Universe Real? From Quaternion & Octonion to Real Coordinates* (Pingree Hill Publishing, Auburn, NH, 2020).

_____, 2020j, *The Origin of Universes: of Quaternion Unified SuperStandard Theory (QUeST); and of the Octonion Megaverse (UTMOST)* (Pingree Hill Publishing, Auburn, NH, 2020).

_____, 2020k, *The Seven Spaces of Creation: Octonion Cosmology* (Pingree Hill Publishing, Auburn, NH, 2020).

_____, 2020l, *From Octonion Cosmology to the Unified SuperStandard Theory of Particles* (Pingree Hill Publishing, Auburn, NH, 2020).

_____, 2021a, *Pioneering the Cosmos* (Pingree Hill Publishing, Auburn, NH, 2021).

_____, 2021b, *Pioneering the Cosmos II* (Pingree Hill Publishing, Auburn, NH, 2021).

_____, 2021c, *Beyond Octonion Cosmology* (Pingree Hill Publishing, Auburn, NH, 2021).

_____, 2021d, *Universes are Particles* (Pingree Hill Publishing, Auburn, NH, 2021).

_____, 2021e, *Octonion-like dna-based life, Universe expansion is decay, Emerging New Physics* (Pingree Hill Publishing, Auburn, NH, 2021).

_____, 2021f, *The Science of Creation New Quantum Field Theory of Spaces* (Pingree Hill Publishing, Auburn, NH, 2021).

_____, 2021g, *Quantum Space Theory With Application to Octonion Cosmology & Possibly To Fermionic Condensed Matter* (Pingree Hill Publishing, Auburn, NH, 2021).

_____, 2021h, *21st Century Natural Philosophy of Octonion Cosmology , and Predestination, Fate, and Free Will* (Pingree Hill Publishing, Auburn, NH, 2021).

_____, 2021i, *Beyond Octonion Cosmology II : Origin of the Quantum; A New Generalized Field Theory (GiFT); A Proof of the Spectrum of Universes; Atoms in Higher Universes* (Pingree Hill Publishing, Auburn, NH, 2021).

_____, 2021j, *Integration of General Relativity and Quantum Theory: Octonion Cosmology, GiFT, Creation/Annihilation Spaces CASe, Reduction of Spaces to a Few Fermions and Symmetries in Fundamental Frames* (Pingree Hill Publishing, Auburn, NH, 2021).

_____, 2022a, *New View of Octonion Cosmology Based on the Unification of General Relativit and Quantum Theory* (Pingree Hill Publishing, Auburn, NH, 2022).

_____, 2022b, *The Dust Beneath Hypercomplex Cosmology* (Pingree Hill Publishing, Auburn, NH, 2022).

_____, 2022c, *Passing Through Nature to Eternity: ProtoCosmos, HyperCosmos, Unified SuperStandard Theory* (Pingree Hill Publishing, Auburn, NH, 2022).

_____, 2022d, *HyperCosmos Fractionation and Fundamental Reference Frame Based Unification: Particle Inner Space Basis of Parton and Dual Resonance Models* (Pingree Hill Publishing, Auburn, NH, 2022).

_____, 2022e, *A New UniDimension ProtoCosmos and SuperString F-Theory Relation to the HyperCosmos* (Pingree Hill Publishing, Auburn, NH, 2022).

_____, 2022f, *The Cosmic Panorama: ProtoCosmos, HyperCosmos,Unified SuperStandard Theory (UST) Derivation* (Pingree Hill Publishing, Auburn, NH, 2022).

_____, 2022g, *Ultimate Origin: ProtoCosmos and HyperCosmos* (Pingree Hill Publishing, Auburn, NH, 2022).

_____, 2023a, *UltraUnification and the Generation of the Cosmos* (Pingree Hill Publishing, Auburn, NH, 2023).

_____, 2023b, *God and and Cosmos Theory* (Pingree Hill Publishing, Auburn, NH, 2023).

_____, 2023c, *A New Completely Geometric SU(8) Cosmos Theory; New PseudoFermion Fields; Fibonacci-like Dimension Arrays; Ramsey Number Approximation* (Pingree Hill Publishing, Auburn, NH, 2023).

_____, 2023d, *Newton's Apple is Now the Fermion* (Pingree Hill Publishing, Auburn, NH, 2023).

_____, 2023e,*Cosmos Theory: The Sub-Particle Gambol Model* (Pingree Hill Publishing, Auburn, NH, 2023).

_____, 2024a, *Cosmos-Universe-Particle-Gambol Theory* (Pingree Hill Publishing, Auburn, NH, 2024).

_____, 2024b, *Fractal Cosmos Theory* (Pingree Hill Publishing, Auburn, NH, 2024).

Eddington, A. S., 1952, *The Mathematical Theory of Relativity* (Cambridge University Press, Cambridge, U.K., 1952).

Fant, Karl M., 2005, *Logically Determined Design: Clockless System Design With NULL Convention Logic* (John Wiley and Sons, Hoboken, NJ, 2005).

Feinberg, G. and Shapiro, R., 1980, *Life Beyond Earth: The Intelligent Earthlings Guide to Life in the Universe* (William Morrow and Company, New York, 1980).

Gelfand, I. M., Fomin, S. V., Silverman, R. A. (tr), 2000, *Calculus of Variations* (Dover Publications, Mineola, NY, 2000).

Giaquinta, M., Modica, G., Souchek, J., 1998, *Cartesian Coordinates in the Calculus of Variations* Volumes I and II (Springer-Verlag, New York, 1998).

Giaquinta, M., Hildebrandt, S., 1996, *Calculus of Variations* Volumes I and II (Springer-Verlag, New York, 1996).

Gradshteyn, I. S. and Ryzhik, I. M., 1965, *Table of Integrals, Series, and Products* (Academic Press, New York, 1965).

Heitler, W., 1954, *The Quantum Theory of Radiation* (Claendon Press, Oxford, UK, 1954).

Huang, Kerson, 1992, *Quarks, Leptons & Gauge Fields 2nd Edition* (World Scientific Publishing Company, Singapore, 1992).

Jost, J., Li-Jost, X., 1998, *Calculus of Variations* (Cambridge University Press, New York, 1998).

Kaku, Michio, 1993, *Quantum Field Theory*, (Oxford University Press, New York, 1993).

Kirk, G. S. and Raven, J. E., 1962, *The Presocratic Philosophers* (Cambridge University Press, New York, 1962).

Landau, L. D. and Lifshitz, E. M., 1987, *Fluid Mechanics 2nd Edition*, (Pergamon Press, Elmsford, NY, 1987).

Misner, C. W., Thorne, K. S., and Wheeler, J. A., 1973, *Gravitation* (W. H. Freeman, New York, 1973).

Rescher, N., 1967, *The Philosophy of Leibniz* (Prentice-Hall, Englewood Cliffs, NJ, 1967).

Rieffel, Eleanor and Polak, Wolfgang, 2014, *Quantum Computing* (MIT Press, Cambridge, MA, 2014).

Riesz, Frigyes and Sz.-Nagy, Béla, 1990, *Functional Analysis* (Dover Publications, New York, 1990).

Sagan, H., 1993, *Introduction to the Calculus of Variations* (Dover Publications, Mineola, NY, 1993).

Sakurai, J. J., 1964, *Invariance Principles and Elementary Particles* (Princeton University Press, Princeton, NJ, 1964).

Weinberg, S., 1972, *Gravitation and Cosmology* (John Wiley and Sons, New York, 1972).

Weinberg, S., 1995, *The Quantum Theory of Fields Volume I* (Cambridge University Press, New York, 1995).

INDEX

About the Author

Stephen Blaha is a well-known Physicist and Man of Letters with interests in Science, Society and civilization, the Arts, and Technology. He had an Alfred P. Sloan Foundation scholarship in college. He received his Ph.D. in Physics from Rockefeller University. He has served on the faculties of several major universities. He was also a Member of the Technical Staff at Bell Laboratories, a manager at the Boston Globe Newspaper, a Director at Wang Laboratories, and President of Blaha Software Inc. and of Janus Associates Inc. (NH).

Among other achievements he was a co-discoverer of the "r potential" for heavy quark binding developing the first (and still the only demonstrable) non-Aeolian gauge theory with an "r" potential; first suggested the existence of topological structures in superfluid He-3; first proposed Yang-Mills theories would appear in condensed matter phenomena with non-scalar order parameters; first developed a grammar-based formalism for quantum computers and applied it to elementary particle theories; first developed a new form of quantum field theory without divergences (thus solving a major 60 year old problem that enabled a unified theory of the Standard Model and Quantum Gravity without divergences to be developed); first developed a formulation of complex General Relativity based on analytic continuation from real space-time; first developed a generalized non-homogeneous Robertson-Walker metric that enabled a quantum theory of the Big Bang to be developed without singularities at t = 0; first generalized Cauchy's theorem and Gauss' theorem to complex, curved multi-dimensional spaces; received Honorable Mention in the Gravity Research Foundation Essay Competition in 1978; first developed a physically acceptable theory of faster-than-light particles; first derived a composition of extremums method in the Calculus of Variations; first quantitatively suggested that inflationary periods in the history of the universe were not needed; first proved Gödel's Theorem implies Nature must be quantum; provided a new alternative to the Higgs Mechanism, and Higgs particles, to generate masses; first showed how to resolve logical paradoxes including Gödel's Undecidability Theorem by developing Operator Logic and Quantum Operator Logic; first developed a quantitative harmonic oscillator-like model of the life cycle, and interactions, of civilizations; first showed how equations describing superorganisms also apply to civilizations. A recent book shows his theory applies successfully to the past 14 years of history and to *new* archaeological data on Andean and Mayan civilizations as well as Early Anatolian and Egyptian civilizations.

He first developed an axiomatic derivation of the form of The Standard Model from geometry – space-time properties – The Unified SuperStandard Model. It unifies all the known forces of Nature. It also has a Dark Matter sector that includes a Dark ElectroWeak sector with Dark doublets and Dark gauge interactions. It uses quantum coordinates to remove infinities that crop up in most interacting quantum field theories and additionally to remove the infinities that appear in the Big Bang and generate inflationary growth of the universe. It shows gravity has a MOND-like form without sacrificing Newton's Laws. It relates the interactions of the MOND-like sector of gravity with the r-potential of Quark Confinement. The axioms of the theory lead to the question of their origin. We suggest in the preceding edition of this book it can be attributed to an entity with God-like properties. We explore these properties in "God Theory" and show they predict that the Cosmos exists forever although individual universes (or incarnations of our universe) "come and go." Several other important results emerge from God Theory such a functionally triune God. The Unified SuperStandard Theory has many other important parts described in the Current Edition of *The Unified SuperStandard Theory* and expanded in subsequent volumes.

Blaha has had a major impact on a succession of elementary particle theories: his Ph.D. thesis (1970), and papers, showed that quantum field theory calculations to all orders in ladder approximations could not give scaling deep inelastic electron-nucleon scattering. He later showed the eigenvalue equation for the fine structure constant α in Johnson-Baker-Willey QED had a zero at $\alpha = 1$ not $1/137$ by solving the Schwinger-Dyson equations to all orders in an approximation that agreed with exact results to 4th order in α thus ending interest in this theory. In 1979 at Prof. Ken Johnson's (MIT) suggestion he calculated the proton-neutron mass difference in the MIT bag model and found the result had the wrong sign reducing interest in the bag model. These results all appear in Physical Review papers. In the 2000's he repeatedly pointed out the shortcomings of SuperString theory and showed that The Standard Model's form could be derived from space-time geometry by an extension of Lorentz transformations to faster than light transformations. This deeper space-time basis greatly increases the possibility that it is part of THE fundamental theory. Recently, Blaha showed that the Weak interactions differed significantly from the Strong, electromagnetic and gravitation interactions in important respects while these interactions had similar features, and suggested that ElectroWeak theory, which is essentially a glued union of the Weak interactions and Electromagnetism, possibly modulo unknown Higgs particle features, be replaced by a unified theory of the other interactions combined with a stand-alone Weak interaction theory. Blaha also showed that, if Charmonium calculations are taken seriously, the Strong interaction coupling constant is only a factor of five larger than the electromagnetic coupling constant, and thus Strong interaction perturbation theory would make sense and yield physically meaningful results.

In graduate school (1965-71) he wrote substantial papers in elementary particles and group theory: The Inelastic E- P Structure Functions in a Gluon Model. Phys. Lett. B40:501-502,1972; Deep-Inelastic E-P Structure Functions In A Ladder Model With Spin 1/2 Nucleons, Phys.Rev. D3:510-523,1971; Continuum Contributions To The Pion Radius, Phys. Rev. 178:2167-2169,1969; Character Analysis of U(N) and SU(N), J. Math. Phys. 10, 2156 (1969); and The Calculation of the Irreducible Characters of the Symmetric Group in Terms of the Compound Characters, (Published as Blaha's Lemma in D. E. Knuth's book: *The Art of Computer Programming Vols. 1 – 4*).

In the early 1980's Blaha was also a pioneer in the development of UNIX for financial, scientific and Internet applications: benchmarked UNIX versions showing that block size was critical for UNIX performance, developing financial modeling software, starting database benchmarking comparison studies, developing Internet-like UNIX networking (1982) and developing a hybrid shell programming technique (1982) that was a precursor to the PERL programming language. He was also the manager of the AT&T ten-year future products development database. His work helped lead to commercial UNIX on computers such as Sun Micros, IBM AIX minis, and Apple computers.

In the 1980's he pioneered the development of PC Desktop Publishing on laser printers and was nominated for three "Awards for Technical Excellence" in 1987 by PC Magazine for PC software products that he designed and developed.

Recently he has developed a theory of Megaverses – actual universes of which our universe is one – with quantum particle-like properties based on the Wheeler-DeWitt equation of Quantum Gravity. He has developed a theory of a baryonic force, which had been conjectured many years ago, and estimated the strength of the force based on discrepancies in measurements of the gravitational constant G. This force, operative in D-dimensional space, can be used to escape from our universe in "uniships" which are the equivalent of the faster-than-light starships proposed in the author's earlier books. Thus travel to other universes, as well as to other stars is possible.

Blaha also considered the complexified Wheeler-DeWitt equation and showed that its limitation to real-valued coordinates and metrics generated a Cosmological Constant in the Einstein equations.

The author has also recently written a series of books on the serious problems of the United States and their solution as well as a book on the decline of Mankind that will follow from current social and genetic trends in Mankind.

In the past twenty years Dr. Blaha has written over 80 books on a wide range of topics. Some recent major works are: *From Asynchronous Logic to The Standard Model to Superflight to the Stars*, *All the Universe!*, *SuperCivilizations: Civilizations as Superorganisms*, *America's Future: an Islamic Surge, ISIS, al Qaeda, World Epidemics, Ukraine, Russia-China Pact, US Leadership Crisis*, *The Rises and Falls of Man – Destiny – 3000 AD: New Support for a Superorganism MACRO-THEORY of CIVILIZATIONS From CURRENT WORLD TRENDS and NEW Peruvian, Pre-Mayan, Mayan, Anatolian, and Early Egyptian Data, with a Projection to 3000 AD*, and *Mankind in Decline: Genetic Disasters, Human-Animal Hybrids, Overpopulation, Pollution, Global Warming, Food and Water Shortages, Desertification, Poverty, Rising Violence, Genocide, Epidemics, Wars, Leadership Failure.*

He has taught approximately 4,000 students in undergraduate, graduate, and postgraduate corporate education courses primarily in major universities, and large companies and government agencies.

He developed a quantum theory, The Unified SuperStandard Theory (UST), which describes elementary particles in detail without the difficulties of conventional quantum field theory. He found that the internal symmetries of this theory could be exactly derived from an octonion theory called QUeST. He further found that another octonion theory (UTMOST) describes the Megaverse. It can hold QUeST universes such as our own universe. It has an internal symmetry structure which is a superset of the QUeST internal symmetries.

Recently he developed Octonion Cosmology. He replaced it with HyperCosmos theory, which has significantly better features. He developed a fractionalization process for dimensions, particles and symmetry groups. He also described transformation that reduced particles and dimensions to a far more compact form. He also developed a precursor theory ProtoCosmos that leads to the HyperCosmos.

The author showed that space-time and Internal Symmetries can be unified in any of the ten HyperCosmos spaces in their associated HyperUnification spaces. The combined set of HyperUnification spaces enable all HyperCosmos dimensions to be obtained by a General Relativistic transformation from one primordial dimension in the 42 space-time dimension unified HyperUnification space.

At present the author devel;oped the Cosmos Theory that incorporates ProtoCosmos Theory, HyperCosmos Theory, Limos Theory, Second Kind HyperCosmos Theory and HyperUnification Spaces. He has introduced PseudoFermion wave functions and theory, He has related Cosmos Theory to Regge trajectories of spaces, parton theory, Veneziano amplitudes, Fibonacci numbers and Ramsey numbers. He has calculated an approximation to the difficult R(n,n) Ramsey numbers.

He has developed a Gambol Model that successfully accounts for e-p deep inelastic scattering, fundamental particle resonances, hadron scattering, and the inner structure of particles based on confinement through Casimir forces of ideal gambol gases. The Gambol Planckian Distribution was derived.

This book derives Cosmos Theory from tensors.